I'M A WELLNESS WITNESS

by

ETTA DIXON

Published in the United States by House of Walker Publishing , LLC (HWP) New Jersey

Permissions: Dazzling Dancer Etta Dixon, Solar Powered Retiree, Reprinted with permission from Molly Charboneau, Assistant Director, DC 37 Communications dept.
Public Employee Press editor Gregory N. Heires
Colonic, Reprinted with permission from George Love
Age is Nothin but a Number, Reprinted with permission from Juan Mercado, Dean of the City College Division of Interdisciplinary Studies
Solar Pioneer, Reprinted with permission from Alison Rose Levy, Author
Library of Congress Control Number: 2018952716
Copyright © 2018 by Etta Dixon
I'm a Wellness Witness
ISBN: 978-0-9834762-8-3

*All dietary suggestions should be discussed with your medical provider before implementing. Nothing in this book should be considered medical advice.

The Power of
prayer

Pray Always
Philippians 4:6-7

Road Map
Psalm 143:8

He Hears, He Answers
Isaiah 65:24

He Knows
Matthew 6:8

Pray This
Matthew 6:9-13

Stay Alert
Matthew 26:41

...ayer

...e gods of
...s, our God
...d our God
...nds. How
...e to realize that
...word we speak,
...thought we think
...er escapes the notice
of our heavenly Father.
He is always listening
for us.

So make it a habit to
be in constant
communication—
anywhere you are.
Any place can be a
place of prayer. The
conversation never
has to stop.

And those times when
you do not know what
to pray or how, ask
the Holy Spirit to help
you and show you
what you should pray
about. He knows us
better than we know
ourselves.

BR🕈ADMAN
CHURCH SUPPLIES
© 2006 Broadman Church Supplies
Nashville, TN. Printed in the USA.
081407011066
www.bhpublishinggroup.com

Letter from the Publisher

Having met Miss Etta Dixon and spending time with her, I was left with an impression of pure wonderment. She's a vibrant, 84-year-old octogenarian, a dynamic force. She epitomizes wellness and wisdom. The many lessons I've learned from her I will practice throughout the rest of my lifetime.

My life has been forever changed by her antidotes, expressed wisdom, and her examples of strength, grace, courage and temperament. She's fearless in her presentation and walks the talk. She captivates an audience with her speech and it all seems to climax into the dance: smooth, happy, inviting and fun.

Miss Etta has left an indelible impression upon my heart and I bestow the greatest of honors to this magnificent woman. She exemplifies the essence of a life well-lived. This work is a testament to that life.

My congratulations to an extraordinary woman! This body of work is an extraordinary feat! And, I thank you.

Much success Miss Etta Dixon. May God continue to Bless you!

Michelle Nelson
CEO & Founder
House of Walker Publishing, LLC

To _Maria Parijis ED_

I'm a wellness witness!

After reading my book, *you* will be a witness of wellness. I hope you will introduce your newfound wellness to all everywhere!

Etta Dixon

MISS ETTA

There is no work like wellness work
so please take pleasure in
accomplishing as much wellness as you
can from the following pages

Introduction

This is my first book. Long after I'm gone, it will still be here for your benefit. Generations to come will benefit from this information.

I was inspired as a teenager from the lyrics of a song, *'Accentuate the positive, eliminate the negative, latch onto the affirmative, don't mess with Mr. in-between'*. It was the best explanation I ever heard about wellness of the brain. These are the lessons I'd like to pass on.

The word wellness in this book should trigger a message to highlight how important your brain is and understanding its important contribution to your wellness.

Grow up as early as you can. Don't wait until you're fifty and be a late bloomer (still better late than never)! Our first childhood is inspired by nursery rhymes such as:

Jack & Jill went up the hill
Mary had a little lamb
An old woman lived in a shoe

I'm introducing, for the first time, literature to inspire those of you in your second childhood. Many of you may not be there yet, but when you get there, I'm sure you will be glad for my little motivational prescriptions.

Many people are subjected to the notion that medicine cures illness. Since our bodies are natural, I refuse to put my delicate organs in jeopardy by medicating, long-term, with chemicals. The secret is that I have never taken any medication long-term so today, at 84 years young, I'm still inspiring others to live a life of wellness…and I tell you how.

My prayer is that you will use my book as a blueprint for your wellness. I'm a wellness witness!

Dedication

I dedicate my book to Ida Robinson, born December 16th, 1923, a forerunner and major contributor of the foundation of wellness principles. Ms. Robinson gave birth to Queen Afua, a recipient of her mother's teachings and now, a champion of healing and training of sacred women in her own right. She's written, *Heal Thy Self,* which encompasses lessons learned from her mother and her vast experience in understanding human anatomy and the mind. Queen Afua gave birth to Ali Torain who learned healthy food preparations at the Heal

Thy Self center that his mother founded. He is a champion of preparing kale salad and raw vegetable salads.

It's an honor for me to have learned the wellness principles and gain an understanding of how medicines are overrated. I seek to awaken others to the natural way of healing that our parents knew.

Read all about it and share your new words of wellness everywhere you go. Be happy about it and I'll be happy to have you as a wellness partner sharing wellness all over the world. I thank you.

I want to introduce you to a different kind of preparedness for wellness. With this book, I hope to create an environment of healing. Keep it in mind throughout the reading of this book.

MISS ETTA

Thinking positive and looking forward
to hearing how this book impacts your
wellness

TABLE OF CONTENTS

Introduction

Dedication   Page

WELLNESS

MISS ETTA AND BERNARD DOVE
SHOWCASING THEIR TALENTS

Get that groove! Dancing is
therapeutic!

My first name is Etta and I guarantee my new suggestions will help you feel better. It is called Dixon's prescriptions. I want you to read all about it! Ponder it. It's time you got onto it! So, let's get to it – the secret is a secret no longer because this book is here to show you how to prepare for excellent healthcare.

My family consisted of my mother and grandfather (who provided for us), me, and my two sisters. Because of their lifestyles, their excessive weight and use of medications to supposedly heal them, I refuse to put my organs in jeopardy with legal drugs. We know a well-trained and well-oiled body will heal itself on its own.

Wellness is one of the sweet kisses of life, so I want you to pursue it and enjoy every bit of it. You are entitled because the best one of the kisses is a kiss of joy. The secret is out. Yes, we'll pull more secrets out as we go along.

Dixon's prescriptions represents wellness. Pick one of the prescriptions to carry with you. Refer to it as often as you can until you're satisfied. Do the same thing with each of the prescriptions.

You will realize the real meaning of healing which is to feel better says Etta! *Oh, how great it is!* Read on to reveal more of what it's all about.

I want you to include your senses (brain). It will clearly show that there is a difference between Dixon's prescriptions and those presently prescribed.

Wellness is rare so be aware of how important it is for you to keep a **HEALING** environment near. Health benefits are what you're looking for. Just remember, it's right between your ears. It's your mindset. Set it early! Set it first and correct it, as soon as possible!

It is your choice to use your vibrant, decision making power. You have the option to choose a stable healthy lifestyle; one that screams loud and clear: Longevity! Longevity! Longevity!

The following script is a conversation between your worn-out body parts if they could talk.

Feet---"I'm tired, I keep pounding the ground and it hurts."

Legs---"You're complaining? I must hold up this body!"

Lungs---"You guys don't have a problem. I have to breathe air in and out to help the body support you. If anyone has the right to complain, it's me!"

Suddenly, heart interrupts, "If you guys don't shut up and keep doing your work, I will quit."

As you can see from the above conversation, our body parts have a lot of work to do. Be ready to give them the help they need, the cooperation to succeed, which is eating healthy most of the time.

If our organs could tell us how harmful a yo-yo diet (repeat weight loss and gain) hurts them, we would be more in harmony with our organs.

For example, smokers can experience painful tears of the lungs because the lungs are crying out for less cigarette smoke so that more oxygen can get in. The alcoholic's liver cries for less alcohol intake for Pete's sake! The kidneys cry for clean, chemical free healing waters each and every day. Kidney replacements are not readily available so caring for them is the key. Open your eyes to these tears. In fact, use every opportunity to keep your eyes and ears open to adding preventative healing habits to your agenda.

Another helpful hint is to never stop your medications cold turkey. Wean yourself off of them. Please wean yourself off all hurtful habits so that each day, you will be healing your temple. Your body parts will thank you. I will thank you, and the Creator will thank you.

DIXON'S

PRESCRIPTIONS

MISS ETTA AND BERNARD

They have healthy chemistry together
He leads, she follows

*D*ixon's prescriptions will result in a positive difference, bringing you closer to healing and also motivate you in the path of wellness.

The following is my main prescription for wellness:

Train Brain

In dealing with healing
Prevention is the intention
Prevention is the cure

Get out of the disease jail
and get on the health trail

The smaller the meal
the greater the deal
to help you feel
a wellness appeal

After the lights go down low
say to extra night-time eating
a loud NO!

We should be satisfied
truly gratified and more
fortified as we decide
that wellness is our ride
and take the super express
to wellness success

How do we handle unnecessary eating?

By washing it away with a bit of wisdom

it will help us to reach our freedom

Take a dose of plants and herbal teas to

replace all sugar and fat

I beg of you - please!

Nourishing food

no matter how crude

will boost your mood

*Alkalize, to stabilize

a very good way to energize

It's no jive

you'll be very much alive

Fried potatoes, no skin, presently indulged

then we graduate to crispy fried chicken

next is the fund-raiser fish fry

Yes, I'm hollering loud and clear –

Grease! Grease! Grease!

Hurry, hurry up! Get the health **POLICE!**

Don't take it for granted

try not to get frantic

about the pathway to health - antics!

Just shout about it from the Atlantic!

Be ready and open to receive wellness

Be willing and be able to be stable

That's how you subtract the disease

from the table

You must wean off the negative

thoughts in order to grow the

positive ones that is much greater

Pasta, potatoes, white bread, white rice

and sweets, are nursing home's treats

A route we don't want to take

so, make it the one you break

Remember, a healthy breakfast, lunch

and dinner are foods from the Creator

There is nothing greater

Eat it, drink it, inhale it, digest it

for nourishment's favor

For a wealth of wellness

make sure you eat greens every day

since it is your organs rejuvenating way

Weight loss is a great loss

it makes the old age syndrome

get lost

Wellness's first gain

will register life without pain

Death is not a right to practice

get the brain involved and joy

will replace that action

The minute you're no longer hungry,

you know what to do

Stop putting food into you

Ashes to ashes dust to dust

we must be health conscience

with a thrust. Why?

It's simple: Our body is The

Creator's temple

We'd be pain free getting

nourishment from a tree

A weekly trip to *Palisades Park

Korean Spa will take our longevity very far

*see appendix

How good it feels

to be a part of the solution

rather than hooked on the pollution?

HEAR YE! HEAR YE! READ ALL ABOUT IT!

MISS ETTA AND BERNARD

We lean on each other for support
Try it!

Yoga is top-shelf for healing especially with its breathing techniques. What should be done every time we move? We should only move on the exhalation which takes the strain off the hardest working organ in our bodies - the heart. No more explanations are needed!

Wellness will take you around the earth
Stress will put you under the earth

Watch out fat! Ingesting foods that irritates your stomach and your intestines helps America's best-selling product – TUMS.

Suggestion: Don't try to go cold turkey to end an addiction. Gradually reduce the addiction (there are exceptions), and at the same time, increase the rehabilitation. This is humanly conducive, proven successful and easier to do.

If we refuse to embrace what is good for us, there will be no strength to refuse what is bad for us. I repeat...gradually wean on the good and wean off the bad until you are an addict no more.

You know who you are!

Dixon's wellness prescriptions will help you become a symbol of wellness in your family and in your community. Sharing the wellness principles will make you an honored family member because true self-healing is rare in families. We all know that the body will heal itself if it is in tune with its healing senses. These powerful senses help you to see the difference in your thoughts about wellness.

Positive thinking opens the eyes to the ease of healing. Just keep on thinking positively and the brain will respond. With this thought trend, you will win.

Reading health materials will jumpstart your healing. Never give up on your pursuit for longevity and a painless, stress-free life. Recognize that happiness is what you receive from what you give.

Reading about health will accomplish those goals as well as encouraging our young people to become readers and read to non-readers. This is how we kill three birds with one stone.

1. Young people can earn money reading to non-readers
2. Young people will get a deeper knowledge of health

3. Non-readers will be informed about information they didn't know about health and wellness.

We work diligently to resist change without realizing that change is the only thing that brings about progress.

The Bible reads:

Once an adult, twice a child
Spread these words around the community
First childhood is babyhood
Second childhood belong to seniors

Meals for both hoods are similar

Knowing this is ingenious

I hope the day will come when our health insurance will be an *assurance* of giving protection and direction toward a healing connection.

If you don't place importance on your wellness for yourself, do it for the sake of your children. In fact, your children and grand-children will enjoy having healthy parents and grandparents to emulate. With every healing step you take, the power of your mind makes the journey great. Enjoy your move toward

wellness and be excited about it! That's
a sure way for its success!

The Rockies may crumble

Gibraltar may tumble

Our powerful, healthy brains

will never allow

your good health to stumble

MISS ETTA AND BERNARD

The Dip
It solidifies wellness and life

-MOTHER'S WIT-
COMMON SENSE
VS
NON-SENSE

IT'S NOT BERNARD!

This is the face of the person
above. Eugene Hammond
Also known as "Ice"

A powerful brain transforms into what might be undercover justice.

****

- You can't teach an old dog new tricks

- Hit the hay

- Let's bury the hatchet

- Kick the bucket

- You will be pushing up daisies

- For Pete's sake

- For cryin out loud

- Du-jigger or thing-a-ma-jig

- Look before you leap

- (He or she) Easy on the eyes

- Ask me no questions and I'll tell you no lies

- You hit the nail on the head

- You get more bees with honey
- You're burning your bridges at both ends
- Don't let the right hand know what the left hand is doing
- Do everything to help yourself and do nothing to hurt yourself
- Every shut eye ain't sleep
- Do your best to kill two birds with one stone
- You are skating on thin ice
- I'm at the end of my rope
- Let sleeping dogs lye
- A mouth shut is not fed
- Even a barrel stands on its own bottom

- It's six in one hand and a half a dozen in the other
- If it was a snake it would have bitten you (when you can't find what you are looking for and it was there all the time)
- I'm between the devil and the deep blue sea (feeling low)
- I rob Peter to pay Paul
- Her word for yes was 'natch'
- Give them a drink (her solution for dirty clothes)
- Her fashion plate - one black dress (adding accessories changed the look and saved money)

- My hands are tied (this meant that was the end of it)
- My back is against a brick wall (this meant that was the end of it)
- You can't take it with you (solving the problem of greed)
- You came here with nothing and you will leave with nothing
- You can't have your cake and eat it too
- You're so figidity you must have ants in your pants
- You made your bed now lye in it
- You make me nervous (not the coffee that she drank!)
- Stop biting off more than you can chew

- Give him/her enough rope, they'll hang themselves
- Smile and the world smiles with you. Cry, you cry alone
- You can live without your wants, but you cannot live without your needs
- I can see trouble is ahead so don't sugarcoat it. Tell it like it is!
- There is a rough road ahead if you put the cart before the horse
- I will beat the living daylight out of you
- I will give you something to cry for
- I brought you into the world and I will take you out
- Don't make a mountain out of a molehill
- So, the cat's got your tongue huh?

- Where there's a will there's a way
- A stitch in time saves nine
- It looks like the grass is greener on the other side
- You don't have a pot to piss in or a window to throw it out of
- The hand that rocks the cradle rules the world
- It knocked me over with a feather (shock)
- A watched pot never boils
- He couldn't touch me with a ten-foot pole
- They're trying to pull the wool over my eyes

- "I'm not little. I'm not big. Common sense says, I'm just right! Since I'm unable to lie to myself, if not now, eventually, I will be just right!"

MISS ETTA AND BERNARD

Joy and fun! We got this!
And… it's healthy!

TIPS
TO JUMP START
WELLNESS

MISS ETTA AND BERNARD

Our signature move which speaks loud and clear. Don't miss it! It's a healthy stretch.

𝓗armful to your beautiful body is excessive saturated oil, salt and sugar – (SOSS). The replacements for these evils are unsaturated oils, sea salt and agave/stevia.

With more oxygen in your system, you will have more balance and control over your body movements and less falls. The three go together – breathe properly, exhale and move on exhalation. This takes the strain off of the heart. It involves training the brain. Continuously take deep breaths which causes healing (a process worth doing since it takes very little effort from you). This information is a best kept secret - but one no longer! Spread the word!

All you gentle ladies are sacred women. This is how Queen Afua sees you. If your techniques need brushing up, enroll in her training program and you'll be certified to heal. Training for *A Sacred Woman's* education reaches as far as Alaska. This is a sisterhood. It's a global learning experience so look out for these trained sacred women! They are coming!

*See appendix

Your birthright is:

1. Health not disease

2. Strength not weakness

3. Joy not sorrow

4. Peace not restlessness

5. Knowledge not ignorance

Such divine heritages are yours to give thought to and allow it to guide you out of the blockages of life.

- Always pursue health before wealth
- Make it a positive version of yourself

- To live in a happy world that we can feel, we know wellness is the essence of the deal

- Keep away from that run - around debilitating grease. If you put it down, you'll have some peace

- Keep away from run - around sugar. When you finally put it down, you'll be sweeter

- Keep away from run - around fat. Just put it down and you'll be correct

- Keep away from run - around salt. Let it go and you'll have no fault (especially with high blood pressure)

- Keep away from the run - around cheese, it constipates

Seniors, are you tired of being shoved into an unhealthy trap? Use the following verse to snap back!

The berry is your food
The herbs are your medicine
The animals are your pets
So now wellness is set

We don't lose our teeth because they are bad. It's the gums that are too weak to hold them. So, take your knuckles and place them on the side of your cheek and push out the old blood from the gums. This causes fresh blood to come into the gums and feed them. Once the gums are fed, you'll keep your teeth. Use the same knuckles and apply them to your temples and fresh blood will come into your temples and relieve your headache. No painkillers needed!!

W*ords no longer used*

Handkerchief

Kerchief

Fetch

Old maid

Whipper snapper

Tea Pout

Hogwash

Hunk – of – madu

Important Words

Important words that creates a stress-free environment when communicating.

- 6 important words: I am sorry. Please forgive me.
- 5 important words: We can work this out
- 4 important words: I will help you
- 3 important words: I like you (like has longevity, love is momentary)
- 2 important words: Thank you
- 1 important word: Us
- Least important word: **Me**

A PLACE OF DEEP THINKING & COMPOSURE

MISS ETTA AND BERNARD

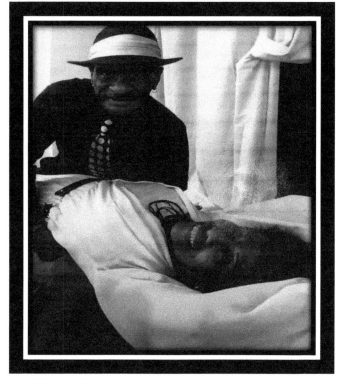

The absolute complete love and
devotion to dance

We elders have something important to say and it will be to your benefit to listen!

Don't you think it would help if politicians added wellness to their mission and at the same time subtract corruption from their ambitions?

Nothing directly happens to you; it happens perfectly for you. Self-esteem is a social role that is mostly earned, not learned. It is a strong support for doing right and no support for doing wrong which is an excellent tool for wellness.

We were intended to squat to have a healthy elimination. With the invention of the toilet bowl, we must improvise the squat position by placing a small bench under our feet; (another healthy living technique). The more fasting and cleansing/purifying you do, the more healing happens to you and you will see yourself transforming to wellness.

Back in the day there was one doctor that administered all care. Today, you are relegated to a series of specialists to treat specific illnesses (ex. diabetes). Now, you are armed with prescriptions that may offer relief but does not heal. It is also inferred that this will be a life-long challenge. I strongly feel that you have a desire to heal.

MISS ETTA AND BERNARD

We're always movin' and groovin'!
Never being still!

ONLY YOU KNOW THE ANSWER

MISS ETTA

This, is the look of wellness

When one is in a relationship, the one test he/she needs to pass is patience-ship. If this is a hardship, you may have to wait for another ship.

How do you treat your mate? With tons of respect I hope. I do want you to know that if you are thinking disrespect is the tool, then you are a fool!

Look in the mirror. What do you see? A friend or an enemy? Please answer correctly for wellness accuracy.

Examples of why we should not put the cart before the horse. Here comes the baby and you should have a rock-bottom foundation ready, a place to put a growing family. If not, there will be no question of who is the boss. It won't be you! It won't be you because the loudest cries get the attention and you know who has the loudest cry!

I'm a wellness witness and I hope you can become one too. Taking a lot of unnecessary medicine for a lot of unnecessary years is ludicrous! I call it a trap! Elders fall frequently in the house, the park, in the shower, etc. This is how they become relegated to live in nursing homes; the place where seniors grow more sedentary. Is this your future? Only you know the answer. So, to this, please give your best brain-thought.

MISS ETTA AND BERNARD

Making independent dance moves

Detoxing

for

Etta Dixon

MISS ETTA AND BERNARD

Looks like we're standing still but the dance goes on as we are movin' and grovin'

Detox your mind in order to detox your body. Every Wednesday I visit King Spa.

First Monday of the month, I go for acupuncture at *Dumisani Kambi-Shamba.

Every season I go to *Elsa for my colonic.

I purchase organic vegetables from *Park Slope Food Co-op.

I purchase fruit Salad from *S & S Fruit & Vegetable Juice Bar.

Now, more of the secrets are out!

*See appendix

MISS ETTA AND BERNARD

This is a leaning step where a woman is supported by the man

ARTICLES OF INTERESTS

MISS ETTA AND BERNARD

Here we go again with our on-going
signature step!

Age is Nothing but A Number

Center for Worker Education (CWE at CUNY) student Etta Dixon, was born a fighter in Brooklyn, NY. Her first battle came in the form of an appendicitis. Doctor's told her family she wouldn't live to be five. Several operations and one-hundred milestones later, Dixon found herself pursuing a BA in Interdisciplinary studies at CWE.

Before coming to the center, Dixon worked for NYC Transit for over 20 years. Now, at the age of 75, Dixon is more active then some people half her age. She works part-time as an elder mother of *Heal Thyself Healing* center and volunteers as a secretary and admitting assistant at Brookdale hospital.

She currently holds a brown belt in karate and makes time for her most loved passion – swing dancing!

Dixon says there were some people who thought she was crazy for going back to school at her age. "I tell them that being a student at CWE keeps the brain away from dementia. Age is a state of mind and being around younger people keeps me young."

Dixon is not a rookie at going against the grain. When she decided to purchase a home as a single woman in 1960's New York, she recalls everyone telling her she was "crazy".

Dixon says she became the first female homeowner in her Brownsville community. Years later, she was the first one on her street to install solar panels on her rooftop.

Professors have described Dixon as an engaging student who is full of energy. Dixon was recently accepted into the Autobiography and Life Experience program.

"I have lots to write about", says Dixon who is the only living member of her immediate family.

Public Employee Press
Etta Dixon: Solar-powered retiree

Etta Dixon on the roof of her Brooklyn home. With the money saved on her heating bills after she installed solar panels, she purchased an eco-friendly car.

*D*ixon has been retired for more than 20 years, but she hasn't slowed down. The former Metropolitan Transit Authority Secretary and Local 1655 member has a busy agenda counseling seniors on health and nutrition issues, volunteering at

Brookdale Hospital and at a local senior center and doing secretarial work several days a week for the DC 37 Retirees Association. Later, the 78-year-old Brooklyn native and her friends like to dance the night away to the sounds of a big band at clubs like the Copacabana.

Dixon is also passionate about protecting the environment. She started recycling long before it became widespread and in 2006, became the first in her Brownsville neighborhood to equip her roof with solar panels that heat water for the two-story, four-family home.

"We don't have to burn fuel, we get free energy from the sun," she explained. She got $5,000 in tax credits and an additional senior citizens discount off the price for the installation, which helps her save an estimated 50 percent on hot water. In 2009, she added new panels that generate all the electricity to light the building's halls and basement.

Always looking for ways to cut costs and protect the environment, Dixon took her considerable savings from the solar panels and bought a Honda Civic with the Eco Assist feature found in some hybrid cars that helps her burn less gas and fill the tank less often.

"If you can save money and stop polluting the air why not?" asked Dixon, who recently started a letter-writing campaign to gather support for tax credits for people who buy hybrid vehicles. "These measures help everyone," explained Dixon. "They create new green jobs and help clean up the environment so everyone down the road can enjoy a healthier lifestyle."

Dazzling Dancer Etta Dixon

By: Molly Charboneau

Public Employee Press, June 2016

"*D*ance, exercise, healthy eating and training your brain are keys to successful and fit aging", says Etta Dixon, 82, a former Metropolitan Transportation Authority secretary, Local 1655, and a DC retiree for more than 20 years.

"In dealing with healing, prevention is the intention", says Dixon describing how she once coached a volunteer at a Kwanzaa event so he could lead her on the dance floor. He said he had been waiting his whole life for someone to show him those steps. That's the type of body movement that keeps us healthy and active.

On May 9th, Dixon was one of five women honored at Clara Lemlich awards for bringing her positive message to seniors citywide with dance instruction

For years, Dixon also performed at meetings and gatherings of the DC37 Retirees Association when she was secretary to their late Vice President of Publicity and Public Relations, Norman O. Davis, her dance partner at those events.

Today, as part of *Mature Magic* with her dance partner Bernard Dove,76, Dixon is active with the *Harlem Swing Dance Society* where she demonstrates swing dance techniques and shares the rich heritage of the Lindy Hop, which originated in the African American community in 1920's and 1930's.

"Dancers like Etta, keeps people involved, engaged, connected and joyful," says Patch Schwadron, of the actor's fund, a former dancer who introduced Dixon at the standing-room only awards ceremony at the Museum of the City of New York's Puffin Gallery for Social Activism. "The energy is always there to leap, take action, listen, watch and send that energy out to others."

With that, the music rang out and Dixon and Dove brought down the house with a rousing swing dance performance that wowed older audience members and awed the younger ones who had only seen such dancing on videos.

A role model

Dixon has been a role model in other areas too. At age 63, she was a multi-medal winner in the Senior Olympics and the first woman on her Brownsville, Brooklyn street, to become a homeowner. At 75, she received her B.A. from The City College of New York and earned a brown belt in karate. In 2012 she was honored as a civic activist by the Office of the Brooklyn Borough for installing energy-saving solar panels on the roof of her home.

For more, watch Etta Dixon's interview at bit.ly/Etta2016 and visit: www.laborarts.org and www.Facebook.org/LaborArts.

A story about her solar panel project appeared in the December 2006 issue of Public Employee Press, which can be read on the union's website at: www.bit.ly/DixonGoesSolar06.

RETIREES ASSOCIATION BULLETIN

June-July 2016

Swing style party

After the business of the June 14th membership meeting was conducted – we partied.

The "Mature Magic of Jazz Swing Dancing" style was demonstrated by our own Etta Dixon and her partner Eugene "Ice" Hammond. They made moves that belied their age and left their audiences awed and breathless. Etta and her partners have been an institution at our parties for years. It seems each performance out-does the last. When you say, "this is as good as it gets", Etta comes back to our next party and tops it.

Our dance class, as always, provided entertainment as well. They demonstrated some new steps and got the audience to join in.

Colonic Irrigation

By Elsa Nteresa

What is a colonic irrigation? It is a process using water to cleanse and restore the colon to perfect health. This cleansing process heals the entire body because areas of the colon correspond to all the glands and organs of the body.

Are colonic irrigations safe?

They are perfectly safe and is excellent for general health maintenance. Only a small amount of water can enter at a time to gently flow up and around the colon.

Are colonic irrigations painful?

There is no pain involved in the entire process; on the contrary, there is relief.

How are colon irrigations different from enemas?

An enema cleans out the lower colon while the colonic irrigation cleans out the entire colon and restores the colon to its normal shape and function.

Who should have colonic irrigations?

Everyone. No matter how perfect your diet may be, a certain amount of waste and mucous accumulates which becomes slime and coats the walls of the colon. This slime, (some go as far back as childhood) is the main cause of most illnesses and irrigating the colon serves as a prevention of diseases.

What are the benefits of colon (CT) therapy?

CT has an antiseptic and solvent action on the intestines - this means putrefactive material, impacted fecal matter, excess mucous, pus and infected tissues are removed from the colon. CT has an anthelmintic action this means parasites are removed.

CT also increases the water absorption level, the diuretic action, the volume of the blood and circulation, resulting in greater bathing of the individual cells, this dilutes toxins and flushes them out. It relieves uremia and toxemia, increases the elimination through both kidneys and skin as well as the bowels. This generally assists the cardiovascular and circulatory systems to be more efficient. Some irrigators have eliminated as much as 10 to 25 pounds just from getting their lower gastrointestinal tract 'cleaned out'.

*Modest Menu for Purifying

Recommended duration: three, seven or twenty-one days

Pre-breakfast

Liver/Kidney flush

8 oz distilled water, fresh lemon

Juice, chopped garlic clove, 1 tbsp

Virgin olive oil, cayenne pepper

Breakfast

Mixed fresh squeezed fruit

Suggested choices: Papaya, apricot, pineapple, pear, peach, apple, berry (blue, black or raspberry)

*see appendix

Lunch: Fresh squeezed mixed vegetable juice

Dinner: Similar to lunch

Ingredients: Carrots, celery, cucumber, green peppers, kale, turnip root, parsley, beets, etc. (at least 4 of the above)

Snacks: (Between juice meals)

Herbal tonic of juniper berry, sage, rosemary

Vitamins:

A: Good multi-vitamin (powdered bio-core)

C: (1500), folic acid, zinc, niacin, lecithin, Dr. Bonner's calcium, Spirulina protein, twin lab super rich yeast

Extra's

1. Enema of water & lemon

2. Epsom salt baths (4-8lbs)

***Consult your physician before implementing. Those with high blood pressure should not attempt.**

SITTING DOWN EXERCISES

Reduces body fat, blood pressure, cholesterol, relieves depression, stress, tension, increases heart efficiency, improves muscle tone.

Start here:

- Bend right elbow, lift left knee so that elbow and knee touch. Alternate with left elbow and right knee creating a pendulum motion. Repeat pattern 5 times.
- Cross arms and embrace yourself 10 times
- Cross arms so that right hand is on left shoulder and left hand is on

right shoulder. Tilt your head from side to side so that your ears touch your hand. Repeat 10 times.

- Extend both legs with toes remaining on floor. Draw right leg back and then left leg back as far as you can 5 times

- Lift elbow as high as you can thrusting your chest forward. Push elbows back as far as you can. Hold position rigid for 7 seconds. Repeat 5 times.

- Lift right shoulder as high as you can then return to starting position. Do the same with your left shoulder. Lift both shoulders twice. Repeat pattern 5 times.

- Lift right knee and wrap your arms around it. Draw it to your chest then place your foot back on the floor. Do the same with your left knee. Hold onto the side of your chair and lift both knees to your chest twice. Repeat pattern 5 times.

- Raise your elbows to chest level. Make four circular motions forward, make four circular motions backward. Repeat entire pattern 5 times.

- Raise legs (right foot then left) off floor as high as you can. Do 10 full flutters.

- Rise right leg and rotate foot 10 times. Put leg back on floor. Do the same with left leg. Raise both legs and rotate feet 10 times.

- Scissors – Extend both legs, alternating legs, cross one over the other 10 times.
- Slide down in your chair and place hands on your waist. Raise arms straight up over your head. Return both hands to your waist. Lean forward touching hands to toes. Return to starting position and repeat pattern 10 times.
- Take a deep breath, hold the air in, bend over with your head pointing to the ground and touch your toes

with your fingers. Sit up and release air. Repeat pattern 3 times.

- Turn your head all the way left, nod 3 times.

- Turn your head right, nod 3 times. Do both 5 times

MISS ETTA AND BERNARD

Watch it, feel it, do it!
The Drop

HEALTHY FAMILY PHOTOS

MISS ETTA

Butterflies added by me!

LUTHER DIXON AND FLORENCE GREENBERG

Executive, songwriter at Scepter
records

HEALTHY CHILDREN RAISED
BY ETTA DIXON

Crystal & twins Robert & Renee
2018-they're over 50

MISS ETTA'S LATE HUSBAND

Luther Dixon, songwriter,
executive, at Scepter Records

MISS ETTA AND HER FIRST DANCE PARTNER CLEMENT POUSSAINT

A dance partnership that lasted over 20 years

HEALTHY CHILDREN OF JENNIFER WARREN, CORPORATE FINANCE LAWYER

Bryce (4) Ella (3) Jordan (5)
2018- 20, 14, 19

MISS ETTA'S PARENTS

Etta and Harold Chase

MISS ETTA AND MARTY MARKOWITZ

Great Brooklyn Borough President
Supporter of solar panel installations in
Brooklyn made his day!

KELLY AND DAVID O'REAR

These healthy children are over 50 today!

MY SISTER MARGARET 5 AND CHUBBY MISS ETTA 2

MISS ETTA AND SAM COLEMAN

MISS ETTA SHOWING OFF
HER AWARDS

MISS ETTA AT 80!

Wanted
Meat Monster

*F*or causing cancer, constipation, irritation and debilitating sugar diabetes. For causing children to be irritable and neurotic. For robbing the body of multi-vitamins. For helping to destroy our teeth, kidneys, pancreas, and committing other crimes against mankind.

Please know, our intestines are thirty-six feet long entwined in the lower stomach.

MISS ETTA AND BERNARD

After the dance is over

Self

Affirmation

MISS ETTA AND HER FIRST DANCE PARTNER CLEMENT POUSSAINT

He taught me everything I know

Fill in the blanks and create a vision

I want to be committed to _____

I'm most proud of _____

I want to move forward with _____

I have this wish for the future _____

I want to savor the_____

I'm grateful for_____

The one thing I will work daily toward

_____

I need _____to succeed

_____is my happiness

Love is _____

My perfect day is _____

To me spirituality is _____

_____is my setback. God

is my come back

My favorite quote is_____

My idea_____

Other_____

Appendix

Foods that Alkalize
(p. 15)

Apples	Asparagus	Celery
Apricots	Broccoli	Hazelnuts
Bananas	Carrots	Honey
Radishes	Cauliflower	Mineral water
Raisins	Green beans	Potatoes
Watermelon	Spinach	Red wine
	Tomatoes	White wine
	Zucchini	

Page: 20 King Spa 321 Commercial St. Palisades Park, NJ.

Page: 44 A Sacred Woman training

Page: 65 Dumisani Kambi-Shamba, (Acupuncture) Masseuse-Flora 305 2nd Ave #2 NYC (212) 447-0750

Page: 65 Elsa (Colonic) 744 St. Johns Place Bklyn, NY (347) 651-3965

Page: 65 Park Slope Food Co-op (Organic vegetables) 782 Union St. bet. 6th & 7th Ave. Bklyn, NY (718) 622-0560

Page: 65 S & S Fruit & Vegetable Stand 92 Livonia Ave. Brownsville, New York 11212 (646) 399-7082

Page: 92 Cleansing/purifying menu

Modest menu for purifying

Extra tidbits for you☺

Queen Afua, author of 6 publications:

Heal Thyself

Training for a Sacred Woman

City of Wellness

Overcoming an Angry Vagina

Circle of Wellness

Planet Heal

(718) 221- 4325 or (929) 351-2140

A & B Publishers

Additional worthy reading:

Lady Prema's 2 publications:

Align with the Devine

Are you Bugging

Publications by Super Nova:

The Remedy

**Free Culinary Training School

69 Belmont Ave Bet Watkins & Osborn St.

Brownsville (Bklyn), NY

Mon -Fri 7am -3pm.

For dance bookings contact: The Harlem

Swing Dance Society at:

theharlemswingdancesociety@gmail.com

Ms. Allison Jones (347) 873-0728

MISS ETTA

Keep pluggin' for wellness

Thank you for your support in reading my first publication. I hope that you will utilize some of the advice I've given.

If you enjoyed this book, you'll be happy to know that a second book titled ***"Let there be Wellness!!!"*** is on its way! Look for it in the future!

Thanks again!

Below are some chapters that will appear in my second book that may be of interest. Topics of wellness:

1. Catalyst
2. Childhood
3. Dance
4. Early
5. Educational
6. Family
7. Financial
8. Human
9. Matrimony
10. Miracle
11. Neighborhood olden day
12. Spiritual

About the Author

Etta Dixon, a Scorpion, was born October 30, 1933 in Brooklyn, NY during the depression. She and her two sisters were vastly different. Their inattention to their health created everlasting consequences which frightened Miss Etta. They both died young and Miss Etta decided early on that that would not be her destiny. She took control of her health and ultimately became a wellness witness.

Throughout her lifetime, she focused on her health and lived and ate accordingly. Dancing became her favorite pastime early in life. She says, *"There was no television, video games or other technological devices so we danced. Young people had to create their own entertainment."*

The Savoy Ballroom in Harlem, NY was a tremendous inspiration for young people to learn how to dance.

In the 1990's she learned everything she now knows about dancing from her first dance partner, Clement Poussaint and have been dancing professionally ever since.

Today, she's a spirited octogenarian who still dances in competitions.

"I tell people that when St. Peter calls, I will tell him that dancing is in my bones and even in the afterlife, I'm hoping to be dancing with my current partner, Bernard Dove."

MISS ETTA AND BERNARD

We're always ready
and looking good!

CPSIA information can be obtained
at www.ICGtesting.com
Printed in the USA
LVHW010753030119
602452LV00003B/3